Inspirational Careers for Kids

When I'm a SURGEON

Dreaming is Believing:
Doctor

samantha pillay

Dr Samantha Pillay

Harry Aveira

Visit
www.samanthapillay.com
to
**Download free coloring pages and resources
Watch free Read-Along video
Order the Activity Book**

#whenimasurgeon

A catalogue record for this
book is available from the
National Library of Australia

Publisher's Cataloging-in-Publication data
Names: Pillay, Samantha, author. | Aveira, Harry, illustrator.
Title: When I am a surgeon : dreaming is believing : doctor / Samantha Pillay ; illustrated by Harry Aveira.
Series: Inspirational Careers for Kids
Description: Norwood, South Australia: Samantha Pillay, 2021. | Summary: What would
it be like to be a surgeon? Come along and explore the wonderful opportunities
of a surgical career. There's more to being a surgeon than you think.
Identifiers: ISBN 978-1-922675-01-9 (hardcover) | 978-1-922675-00-2 (paperback) | 978-1-922675-02-6 (ebook)
Subjects: LCSH Surgeons--Juvenile fiction. | Medical care--Juvenile fiction. | Physicians--
Juvenile fiction. | CYAC Surgeons--Fiction. | Medical care-- Fiction. | Physicians--Fiction.
| BISAC JUVENILE FICTION / Business, Careers, Occupations | JUVENILE FICTION / Girls
& Women | JUVENILE FICTION / Social Themes / Self-Esteem & Self-Reliance
Classification: LCC PZ7.1.P5535 Wh 2021 | DDC [E]--dc23

Dedicated to children everywhere:

Dream big, aim high.

When I'm a surgeon,
I'll be called doctor.

When I'm a surgeon,
I'll stitch people better.

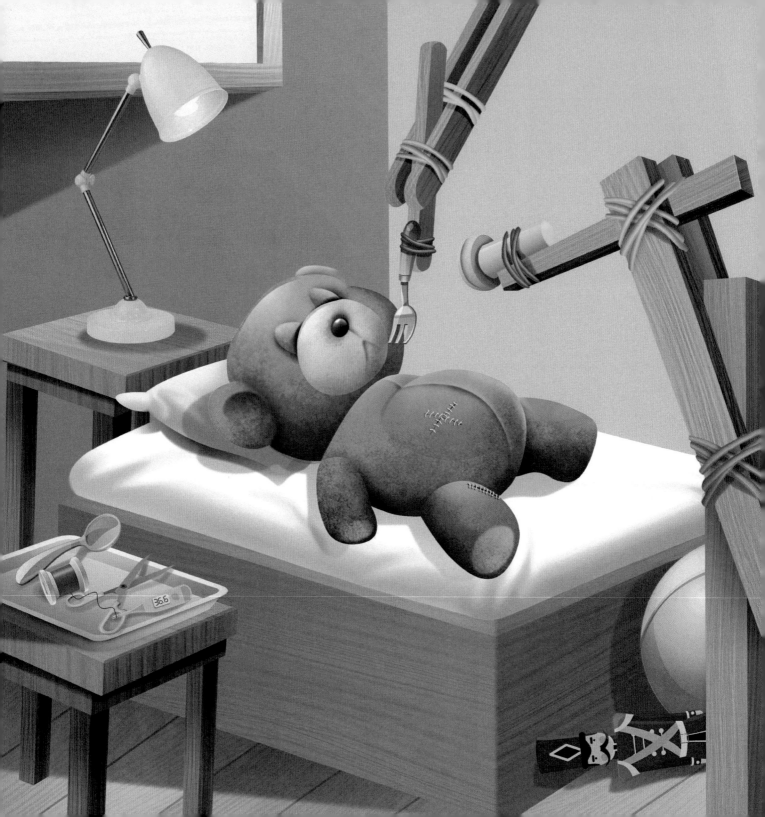

When I'm a surgeon,
I'll work with a robot.

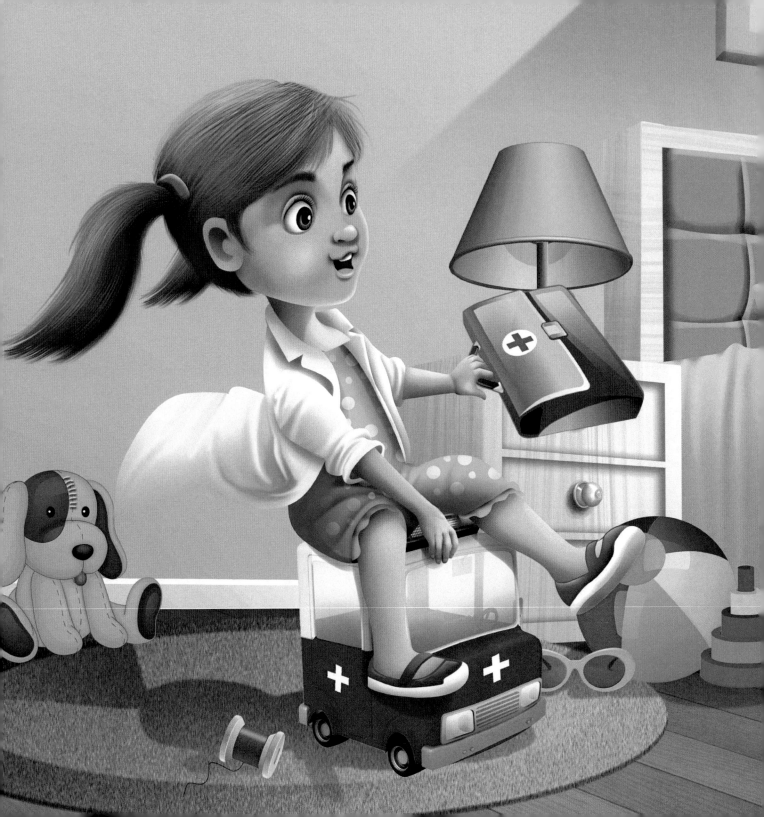

When I'm a surgeon,
I'll deal with emergencies.

Lemonade
Charity
Fundraiser

$1

When I'm a surgeon,
I'll care for the community.

When I'm a surgeon,
I'll teach and train others.

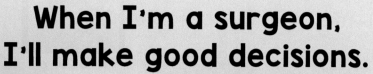

When I'm a surgeon, I'll make good decisions.

When I'm a surgeon,
I'll always be learning.

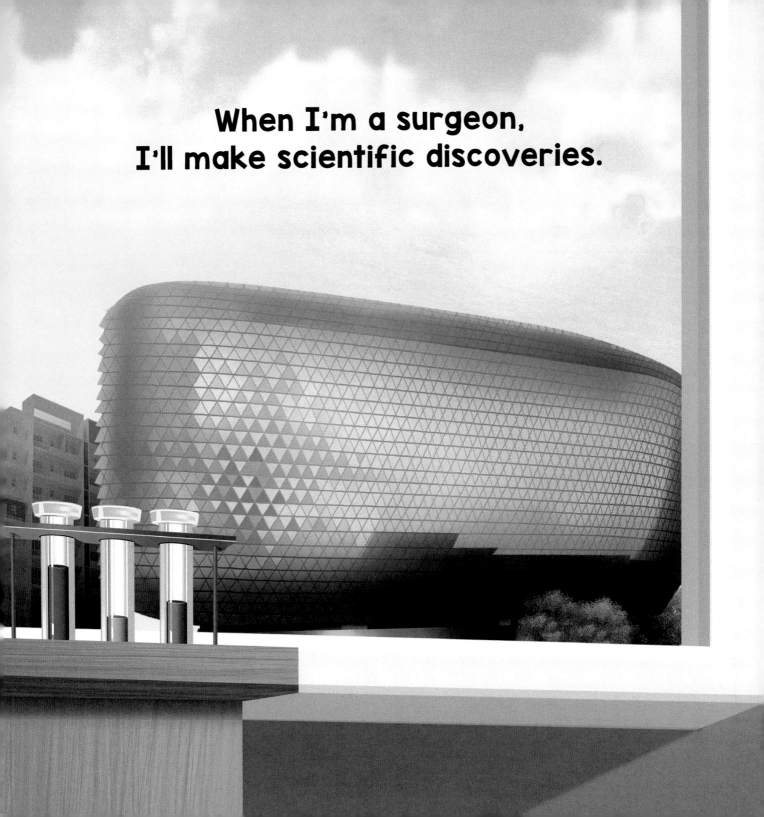

When I'm a surgeon,
I'll make scientific discoveries.

When I'm a surgeon,
I'll travel the world.

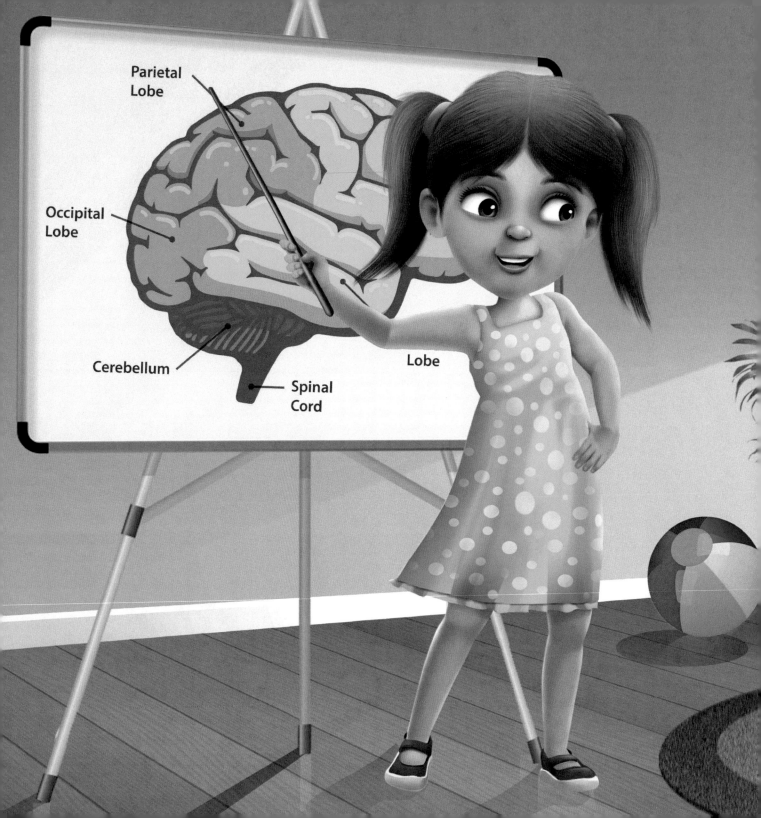

Parietal
Lobe

Occipital
Lobe

Cerebellum

Spinal
Cord

Lobe

When I'm a surgeon,
I'll be a great public speaker.

When I'm a surgeon,
I'll be an inspirational leader.

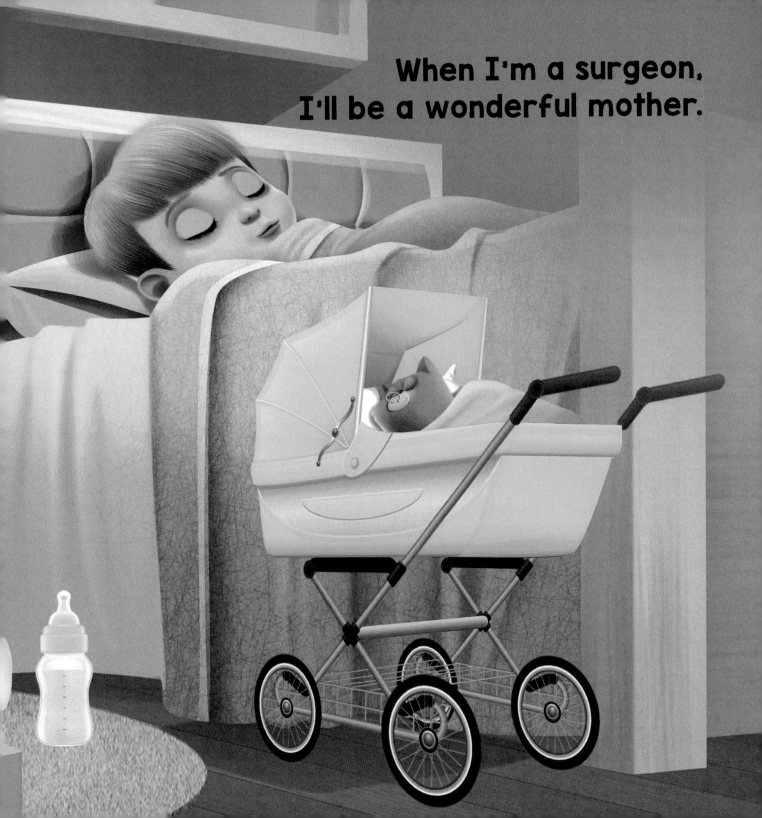

When I'm a surgeon,
I'll be a wonderful mother.

ABOUT THE AUTHOR

SAMANTHA PILLAY, a urological surgeon, is no stranger to overcoming adversity to achieve her goals. Born with hip dysplasia, she underwent several operations, spending about 18 months in hospital from age two to four years. She then started school in a wheelchair, taking years to learn to walk.

With limited mobility and constant pain, unable to participate in sport and many other activities, she loved reading and focused on her studies instead.

She completed school age 16 years and became the first female to complete urological surgical training in South Australia, establishing Continence Matters in 2002.

She began writing in her spare time in 2020, publishing The No Recipe Cookbook – a cookbook for people who don't cook.

Samantha aims to break stereotypes around surgical training for women with her "If I can do it, so can you" message. She advocates for the advantages of surgery as a career for women and its benefits to parenting and family life.

Visit **www.samanthapillay.com** for
Free colour page downloads and Read-along video
Book Two: **When I'm an Entrepreneur** due out soon!

ABOUT THE ILLUSTRATOR

HARRY AVEIRA has been creating children's books for twenty years with more than a hundred books (and counting). He loves partnering with authors to help bring their stories to life. Harry lives in Indonesia with his two daughters and his wife.

Also available at online retailers:

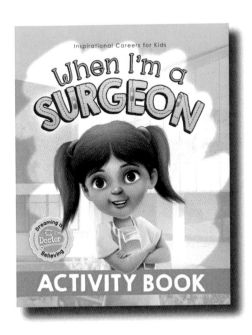

AUTHOR'S NOTE

Surgical training takes commitment and determination. I hope to inspire young girls to find the passion required to pursue a rewarding career in surgery. Misconceptions about a surgical career, when combined with parenting, have contributed to low rates of female surgeons, increasing from 4 to 14% in twenty years, despite 50% female medical students in Australia.

Following an English tradition, male surgeons in Australia have been called Mister, dating back to early surgeons not holding a medical university doctorate. This distinction became a status symbol to distinguish surgeons from their medical doctor colleagues. This tradition only adds to the confusion for female surgeons retaining the doctor title, who struggle to be identified as the surgeon in the medical team.

I am proud to feature two iconic South Australian buildings in this book. The Royal Adelaide Hospital (since rebuilt) is where my father and I trained. The South Australian Health and Medical Research Institute (SAHMRI) building is home to about 700 researchers collaborating nationally and internationally.

Being a surgeon creates opportunities beyond society's perceptions of the traditional role. I am grateful for developing skills beyond my expectations. Operating on someone to help them is a wonderful privilege, yet being a surgeon is so much more than that.

I believe that the advantages for surgical mums outweigh the sacrifices. Surgery has taught me communication, leadership, wisdom, judgment, financial literacy, stress management, decision- making under pressure, teaching and training others, and handling a crisis - often in the middle of the night. What better training is there for a parent?

Made in the USA
Las Vegas, NV
26 October 2024

10490043R10024